2

ASONAWO AHAHAMONO EMAA DA

(ahs-OHN-awoh ah-ahamo-no e-MAH da)

The Asante social system has seven main families. Each family has its own responsibilities and rights. This cloth represents "the green snake of the Asona," one of the seven families.

3

FATHIA FATA NKRUMAH
(fa-THEA fah-TA n-KROH-mah)

The translation for the
name of this pattern is
"Fathia is a befitting wife
for Nkrumah." Fathia
was a charming Egyptian
woman who married
Nkrumah, the first
president of the Republic
of Ghana. Their marriage
was considered special
because it represented
the unity of African peoples
on the continent.

Daniell Allen Kurnick

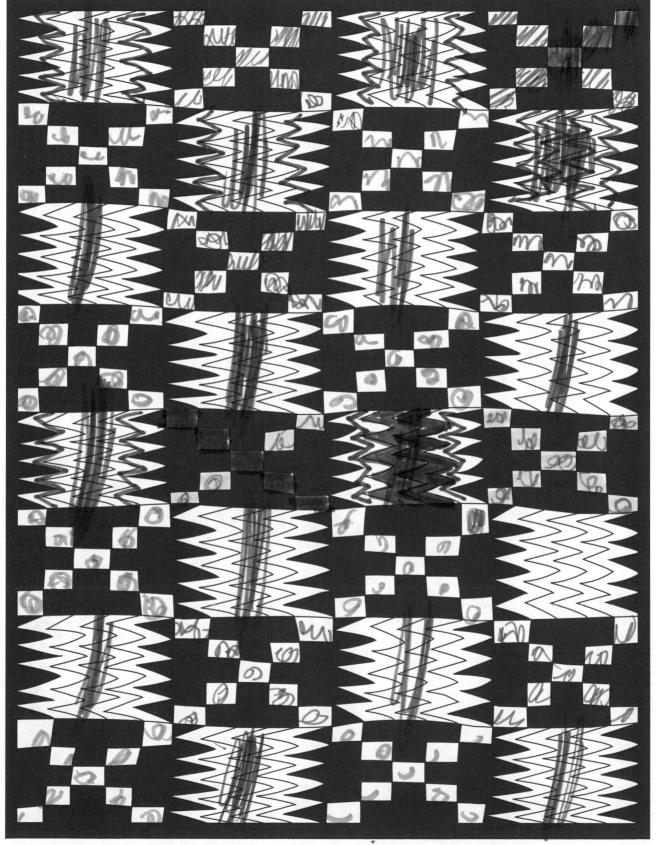

4

ABUSUA YE DOM

(AH-boo-soo-ah yeh dohm)

The name for this pattern means "the extended family is a force." This cloth celebrates the extended family and its important role in maintaining the well-being of its members.

5

AFOAKWA MPUANKRON

(AH-foha-quah M-PUA-n-kr-ohn)

This cloth honors the
trusted royal attendants
and guards. The name
means "Afoakwa of the
Nine Tufts." Afoakwa
was the name of one of
these attendants.
The attendants are
identified by a special
haircut called the
"nine-tuft" haircut.

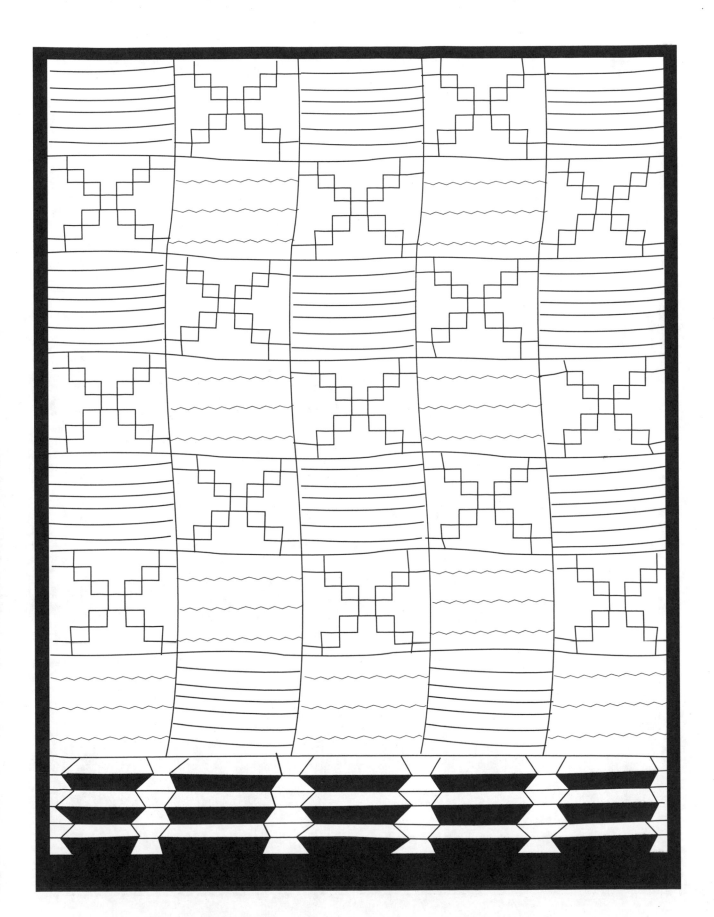

6

OYOKOMAN
(OYOH-ko-mahn)

**This pattern gets its
name from that of the
Asante royal family.
The cloth symbolizes
royalty, nobility,
elegance, and
effective leadership.**

7

ADWOA KOKOO
(AH-joh-a kaw-kaaw)

The name for this pattern means "Adwoa of the reddish complexion." It was designed to honor a wife of a weaver. When this pattern was presented to King Kwaku Dua I (1838-1867), he declared that it could only be worn by his wives to honor their important role in society.

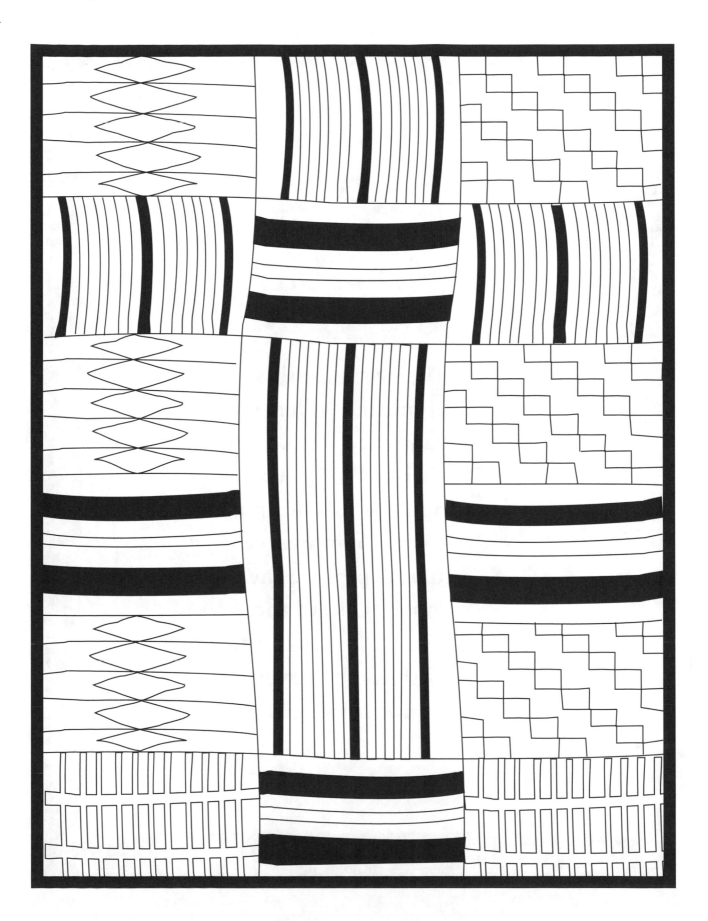

8

EMAA DA
(e-MAH da)

The name for this
cloth means "it has not
happened before."
When one of the Asante
kings saw this design,
he was so impressed
that he praised the
uniqueness of the
pattern. After that, the
cloth was reserved
for royalty.

9

ANKONAM

(ANKO-nahm)

The name of this cloth
means "I walk alone."
The pattern is a reminder of
situations in which a
person has to be strong,
believe in one's self, and
act on his or her own.
Sometimes a person has to
stand alone and not be
influenced by others' opinions.

10

EPIE AKYI

(EH-pee AH-chee)

The translation for
the name of this pattern is
"behind the defensive
wall"or "an encampment." It
refers to the Asante wartime
custom of keeping
women, children, sick
people, and people with
special skills in a camp
where they were protected
from the enemy.

11

NKONTOMPO NTOMA

(n-KOH-n-tom-po n-TOE-mah)

The name of this
cloth is "the liar's
cloth." It serves as a
reminder that
lying and dishonesty
are wrong. The
pattern shows a line
that moves in a
crooked way, much
like the behavior
of a liar.

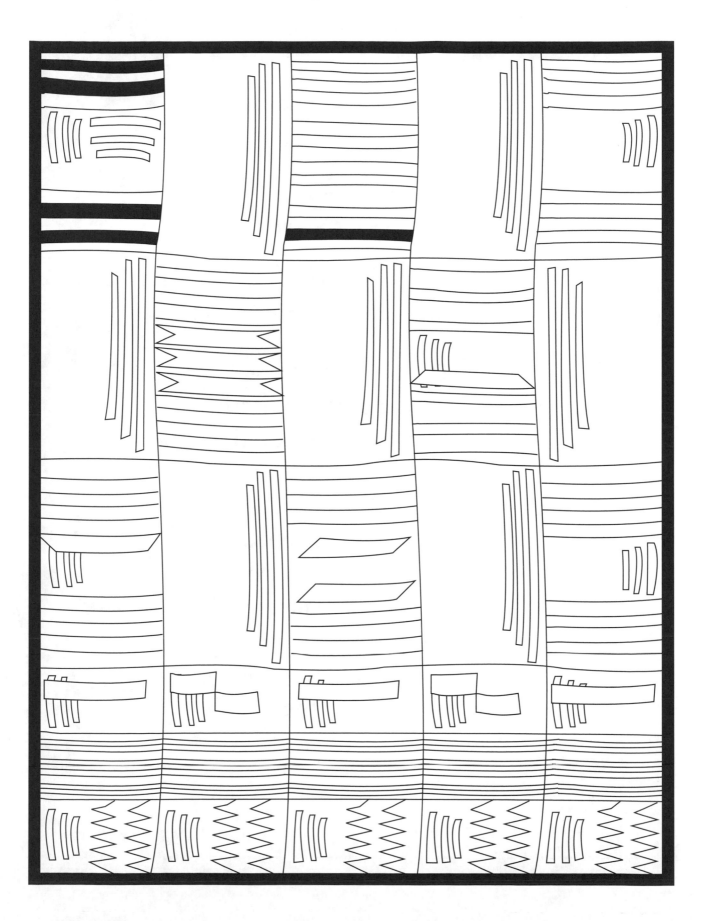

12

FAHIA KOTWERE AGYEMAN

(FAH-hia kawt-were AH-je-mahn)

The translation for
the name of this pattern
is "lean on Agyeman, the
redeemer of the nation,
when in need." The
message is that needy
people should not worry
because their leaders will
help them. Wealthy
rulers should use their
riches to benefit the people.

13

SE WO BEKA ME HO ASEM A MA ME MA WO ADWA NA TENA ASE

(seh woa BE-kah meh hoe ah-sem a mah me mah woa AH-dwa nah TEH-na AH-se)

The literal meaning of this title is "if you have something to say about me, let me first give you a stool to sit on." The stool is for a person who is about to gossip. It represents an invitation to be truthful face-to-face and not tell tales behind another person's back. Thus the pattern represents the disapproval of gossip.

14

OHENE AFRO HYEN
(OH-hen-eh AH-fro sheng)

The name for this cloth is translated to mean "the king has boarded a ship." It was designed to celebrate a special event. In 1937, King Prempeh II crossed the Pra River at the beginning of his journey to England. Before this event, the kings of Asante were forbidden to cross the Pra River as a sign of respect for an Asante king who was killed while doing so.

15

BESEHENE

(BEH-se-hen-eh)

This title means "king of cola nuts." The pattern was inspired by the cola nut, which is chewed for energy and is used to flavor soft drinks. The zigzag design represents cola nuts arranged in their shells.

16

SIKA FUTORO
(seek-AH foo-too-row)

The name of this
pattern translates as
"gold dust." Long ago,
gold dust was used as
money. This cloth
represents wealth,
elegance, and
honorable achievement.

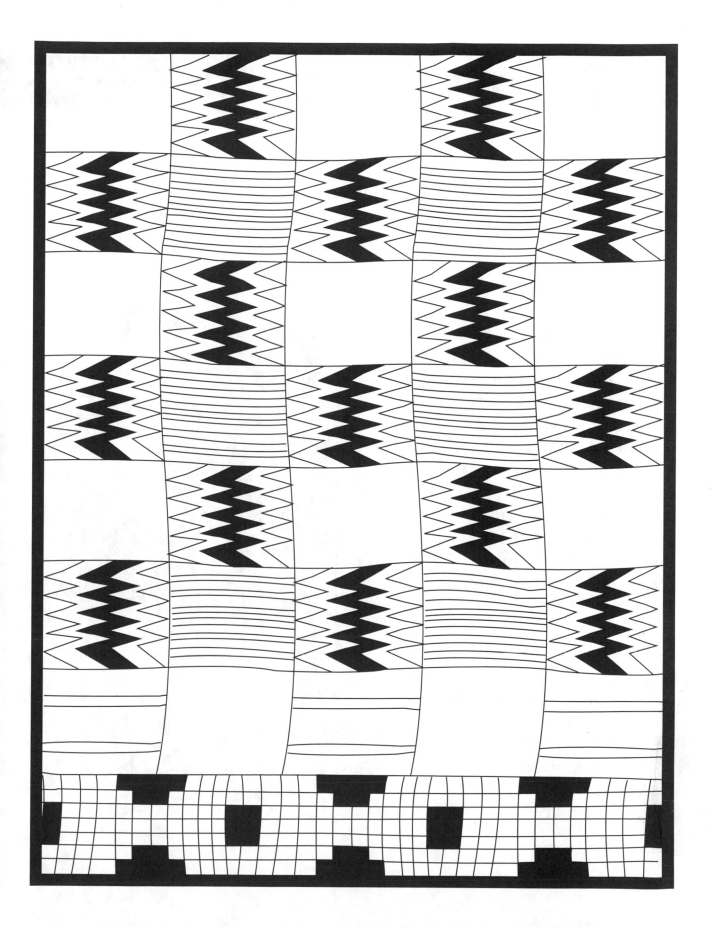

Kente is more than a cloth. It is also a visual representation of various aspects of Asante life. Originally, kente was reserved for royalty, and it was only used for special occasions. As more and more weavers created kente cloth, it became more plentiful and more people were able to buy it.

Today, copies of kente designs can be both machine woven and printed on cloth. The original handwoven designs, however, are still considered to be very precious. Kente cloth is usually worn for ceremonies, festivals, and other sacred occasions. It is also given as a gift for weddings, child naming ceremonies, graduations, and other special events.

When a man wears kente cloth, he usually wears one large piece wrapped around his body, with the right shoulder and hand uncovered. A woman wears either a large piece or a combination of two or three pieces that are wrapped around her body.